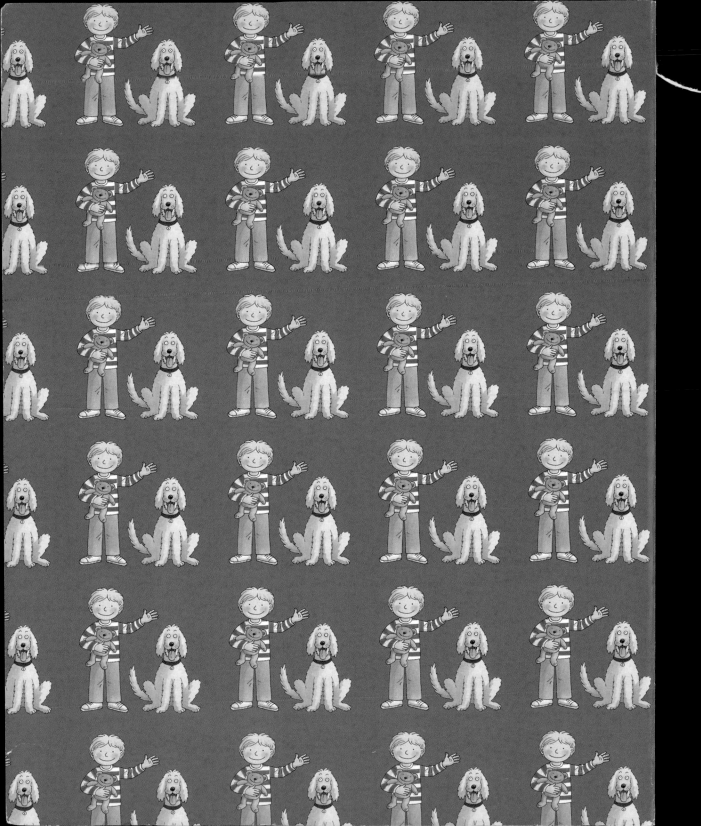

This book belongs to ...

....

OXFORD

UNIVERSITY PRESS

Great Clarendon Street, Oxford, OX2 6DP,
United Kingdom

Oxford University Press is a department of the University of Oxford.
It furthers the University's objective of excellence in research, scholarship,
and education by publishing worldwide. Oxford is a registered trade mark of
Oxford University Press in the UK and in certain other countries

ISBN: 978-0-19-273437-2

3 5 7 9 10 8 6 4

Typeset in Edbaskerville

Paper used in the production of this book is a natural, recyclable product made
from wood grown in sustainable forests. The manufacturing process conforms
to the environmental regulations of the country of origin.

Acknowledgements;
Series Editors: Kate Ruttle, Annemarie Young

READ WITH
Biff,
Chip &
Kipper

Hairy-Scary Monster
and Other Stories

OXFORD
UNIVERSITY PRESS

Tips for Reading Together

Children learn best when reading is fun.

- Talk about the title and the picture on the front cover.

- This book practises some new letter patterns as well as revisiting others. Find the following letter patterns in the story and talk about the sound they make when you read them: *le* as in *uncle*, *oi* as in *coin*, *ow* as in *down*, *ou* as in *cloud*, *er* as in *dinner*, *oe* as in *toe* and *o* as in *go*.

- Look at the *le*, *oi*, *er*, *ow*, *ou*, *oe* and *o* words on page 4. Say the sounds in each word and then say each word (e.g. *u-n-c-le*, *uncle*; *t-oe*, *toe*; *g-r-ou-n-d*, *ground*).

- Read the story then find the *le*, *oi*, *er*, *ow*, *ou*, *oe* and *o* words.

- Talk about the story and do the fun activity at the end of the book.

Have fun!

Children enjoy re-reading stories
and this helps to build their confidence.

After you have read the story, see how many different creatures you can find.

The main sounds practised in this book are 'le' as in *uncle*, 'oi' as in *coin*, 'ou' as in *out* and *down*, 'er' as in *dinner*, 'oe' as in *toe* and *go*.

For more hints and tips on helping your child become a successful and enthusiastic reader look at our website www.oxfordowl.co.uk.

Uncle Max

Written by Roderick Hunt
Illustrated by Nick Schon,
based on the original characters
created by Roderick Hunt and Alex Brychta

OXFORD
UNIVERSITY PRESS

Read these words

uncle	down
coin	out
cloud	noise
toe	go

There was a noise outside the house.
An old car stopped with a bang and a big
cloud of smoke.

An odd-looking man got out. He had long, white hair, a flowing blue cloak and a big, green hat.

The man took out a huge case from
the back of the car.

"Who is he?" asked Biff.

"He's my Uncle Max," said Dad. "I have not seen him since I was a little boy."

"I have been in Peru, and all over the place," said Uncle Max, "but now I'm back."

"Nice to meet you," Uncle Max said to the children. "How do you do?"

"May I stay with you for a day or two?"
went on Uncle Max. "I won't be
a nuisance."

"Uncle Max has lots of cases," said
Dad. "It may rain, so we need to get
them inside."

Uncle Max had a parrot called Sue.
"She's quite shy," said Uncle Max.
"And she's quite rude," said Biff.

The children liked Uncle Max. He showed them a trick. He made a coin vanish.

"Look in your pockets," said Uncle Max. "See! Kipper has it."

Mum liked Uncle Max, too. He made a big pot of stew for dinner.

It looks yummy.

"It's made of dragons' tails and goblins' toes," said Uncle Max.

Uncle Max had a tale to tell.

"Sit down and I will tell you about my escape from a snake," he said.

"I was in Peru when a giant snake slid out of a tree. Its coils wound round me," said Uncle Max.

"But I knew the song of the snake,

… so I sang to it in a deep voice …

… the snake's coils unwound.

Then it lay on the ground and
went to sleep."

"This is my ice cream machine," said Uncle Max.

"What kind of ice cream would you like? I can make red, pink, blue or green."

The ice cream machine began to rattle and shake.

There was a flash and a bang.
The ice cream machine blew up.

"Look at my shed," said Dad.

"Er… do you fancy hot, black ice cream?" said Uncle Max.

"Time to go," said Uncle Max.
"I will come and stay again, soon."

Talk about the story

When did Dad last see Uncle Max?

What story did Uncle Max tell about the snake?

What did Mum and Dad think when the shed blew up?

What stories do you like to tell?

A maze

Help Uncle Max find his parrot.

Tips for Reading Together

Children learn best when reading is fun.

- Talk about the title and the picture on the front cover.
- Identify the letter patterns *oo* and *u* in the title, and the letter pattern *oul* in the story, and talk about the sound they make when you read them ('oo' as in *wood*).
- Look at the *oo*, *u* and *oul* words on page 4. Say the sounds in each word and then say each word (e.g. *p-u-dd-ing, pudding; g-oo-d, good; c-oul-d, could*).
- Read the story then find the words with *u*, *oo* and *oul*.
- Talk about the story and do the fun activity at the end of the book.

Children enjoy re-reading stories and this helps to build their confidence.

After you have read the story, see how many different animals you can find in the pictures of Pudding Wood.

The main sound practised in this book is 'oo' as in *wood*, *bush* and *could*.

For more hints and tips on helping your child become a successful and enthusiastic reader look at our website www.oxfordowl.co.uk.

Save Pudding Wood

Written by Roderick Hunt
Illustrated by Nick Schon,
based on the original characters
created by Roderick Hunt and Alex Brychta

OXFORD
UNIVERSITY PRESS

37

Read these words

pudding	good
foot	hook
could	bush
would	should

Chip and Craig went to Pudding Wood.
Craig's dad took them.

Craig loved Pudding Wood. He was good at seeing birds and animals.

"I can see a woodpecker," said Craig.
"Look. It's up in that tree."

"Look," said Craig. "Can you see that deer? It's by that bush."

"Sssh! Keep still," said Craig's dad.
"Look at the foot of that big tree.
It's a treecreeper."

They met Wilma and her dad.

Wilma had bad news.

"It's Pudding Wood," she said.

"They want to chop it down and put up houses."

They ran back as fast as they could.

"It's bad news," said Chip. "They want to cut down Pudding Wood."

"Could they?" said Biff.

"Would they?" said Mum.

"They couldn't," said Gran.

"I think they could," said
Wilma's dad.

"It would be really bad to chop down Pudding Wood," said Mum.

"Well, can we stop them?" said Gran.

"We could call a meeting," said Craig.

They had a meeting in the hall.
The hall was full.

Craig's dad made a speech.

"We must stop them by hook or by crook," he said.

"Look at my photos of
Pudding Wood," said Craig.

"It has bluebells . . .

54

. . . and deer,

. . . and lots of birds.
I love Pudding Wood."

They all gave Craig a cheer.
"Let's go to the Town Hall,"
called a man.

"We could make a big banner and take it with us," said a woman.

The next day they all went to
the Town Hall. Mum had made a
big banner.

Craig had made a banner, too. He put
it on his wheel-chair.

At last there was good news.
Pudding Wood was saved.

"I should think so, too," said Biff.
"The birds and animals need
Pudding Wood."

Pudding
Wood
is good!

"We need Pudding Wood too,"
said Craig.

Talk about the story

What did Craig and Chip see in the wood on their visit?

What was Wilma's bad news?

How did Craig's photos help to save Pudding Wood?

What do you look out for when you go to the woods?

Which one?

The 'oo' sound can be spelled *oo, oul* or *u*. Can you choose the correct spelling for these words? Look back in the story to check if you are right.

w____d

w____d

p__dding

sh____d

g____d

Tips for Reading Together

Children learn best when reading is fun.

- Talk about the title and the picture on the cover.

- Discuss what you think the story might be about.

- Read the story together, inviting your child to read as much of it as they can.

- Give lots of praise as your child reads, and help them when necessary.

- If they get stuck, try reading the first sound of the word, or break the word into chunks, or read the whole sentence again. Focus on the meaning.

- Re-read the story later, encouraging your child to read as much of it as they can.

Children enjoy re-reading stories and this helps to build their confidence.

Have fun!

After you have read the story, find all the mini monsters in the pictures.

This book includes these useful common words:
laughed   something   under   behind

For more hints and tips on helping your child become a successful and enthusiastic reader look at our website www.oxfordowl.co.uk.

Hairy-Scary Monster

Written by Cynthia Rider
based on the original characters
created by Roderick Hunt and Alex Brychta
Illustrated by Alex Brychta

OXFORD
UNIVERSITY PRESS

Kipper didn't want to go to sleep.
"Biff and Chip are at Gran's," he
said. "I don't like being on my own."

"Poor Kipper," thought Floppy.
"I'll stay with him."
"Oh no, Floppy," said Mum.
"Kipper is going to sleep."

But Kipper wasn't going to sleep.
He was wide awake.

"I can't go to sleep," he grumbled.
"I just can't!"

Kipper laughed. "I know! I'll play
a trick," he said. "I'll trick Dad and
get him to come upstairs."

He jumped up and down on his bed. "Dad!" he yelled. "There's a hairy-scary monster! It's coming to get me, Dad. Help!"

Dad ran up to Kipper's bedroom.
Floppy barked and ran after him.
"What monster?" said Dad.
"Where is it?"

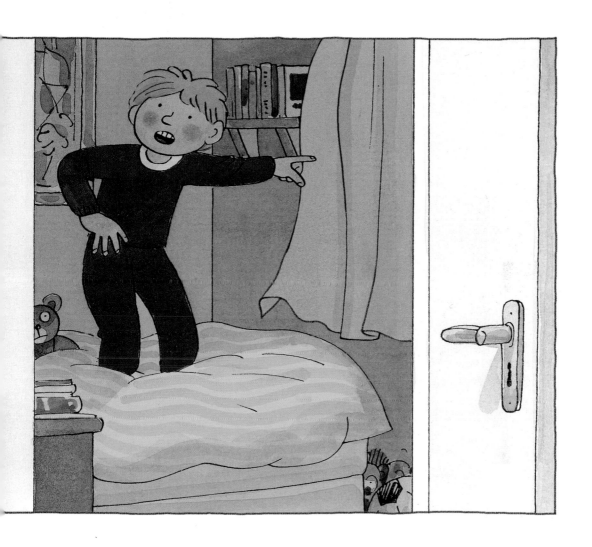

Kipper pointed to the curtains.

"It's behind the curtains," he said.

"It's got sharp yellow teeth and
glowing red eyes."

Dad looked behind the curtains,
but he didn't see a monster.

"There's no monster here," he
said. "Look!"

"It was a trick," laughed Kipper.
"It was just a trick!"

Dad laughed, and tucked Kipper
up. "Be a good boy and go to sleep,"
he said. "And no more tricks!"

Floppy was hiding. He didn't
like monsters.

"Come out, Floppy," said Dad.
"Kipper is going to sleep."

But Kipper wasn't going to sleep.
He was still wide awake.

"I don't like being on my own,"
he grumbled. "It's boring."

Kipper laughed. "I know! I'll play
another trick," he said. "I'll trick
Mum and get her to come upstairs."

"Mum!" yelled Kipper. "There's a hairy-scary monster! It's going to eat me up. Mum, help!"

Mum ran up to Kipper's bedroom.

Floppy barked and ran after her.

"What monster?" said Mum.

"Where is it?"

Kipper pointed to the wardrobe.
"It's in the wardrobe," he said.
"It's got long sharp claws and
hairy jaws."

Mum looked in the wardrobe, but she didn't see a monster.

"There's no monster here," she said. "Look!"

"It was a trick!" laughed Kipper.
"It was just a trick."

Mum tucked Kipper up again.
"Be a good boy and go to sleep,"
she said. "And no more tricks!"

Kipper began to fall asleep. His
eyes were just closing when he heard
something under the bed.

It was something that was snuffling.
It was something that was snorting.
It was something that was hairy and
very, very scary!

"Help!" yelled Kipper. "There really is a monster! Mum, Dad, help me! I'm scared!"

Mum and Dad ran upstairs.

"What's wrong, Kipper?" they said.

"There's a monster," he sobbed.

"There's a monster under the bed."

Dad looked under the bed.

"There is a monster!" he said. "It's
the Hairy-Scary Floppy Monster!"

Talk about the story

Why didn't Kipper want to go to sleep?

Which three places did Kipper say the monster was hiding?

What things made you laugh in the story?

What makes you scared?

Hide and Seek

What is the monster hiding from? Find the words that
rhyme. The words that are left tell you what the monster
is hiding from.

claws

trick

hairy

man

mouse

little

pan

stick

jaws

scary

Tips for Reading Together

Children learn best when reading is fun.

- Talk about the title and the picture on the front cover.

- Discuss what you think the story might be about.

- Read the story together, inviting your child to read as much of it as they can.

- Give lots of praise as your child reads, and help them when necessary.

- If they get stuck, try reading the first sound of the word, or break the word into chunks, or read the whole sentence again. Focus on the meaning.

- Re-read the story later, encouraging your child to read as much of it as they can.

Children enjoy re-reading stories and this helps to build their confidence.

Have fun!

After you have read the story, find the 10 hiking boots hidden in the pictures.

This book includes these useful common words:
suddenly   shouted   station   climbed/climbing/climber

For more hints and tips on helping your child become a successful and enthusiastic reader look at our website www.oxfordowl.co.uk.

Mountain Rescue

Written by Cynthia Rider
based on the original characters
created by Roderick Hunt and Alex Brychta
Illustrated by Alex Brychta

OXFORD
UNIVERSITY PRESS

Biff was showing Wilma her new
music box.

"It's like a little house," said Wilma.

Biff opened the box and the music
began to play. Suddenly, the magic
key began to glow.

The magic took Biff and Wilma
to a mountain railway station.
"The station looks just like my
music box," said Biff.

There was a big wooden horn
at the station. A boy called Max told
them that it was used to send for the
Mountain Rescue helicopter.

"My Uncle Hans flies the helicopter," he said. "He's taking me to see an eagle's nest today. You can come with us."

The children got into a train. It took them higher up the mountain. Uncle Hans was waiting at the station.

"Hi Max," said Uncle Hans. "I'm
glad some of your friends have
come with you."

Uncle Hans and the children went
up a steep track. They saw some
people climbing a steep rock.

"That looks scary!" said Biff.

Just then, Uncle Hans's phone
rang. "I have to go back, but you
can see the eagle's nest from here,"
he said.

The eagle was sitting on her nest.
Suddenly, she squawked and flew
into the sky.

"A man has climbed up to the
nest!" said Biff. "He's putting the
eagle's egg into his bag."

"Put that egg back!" shouted
Wilma.

The man looked up. He saw the
children watching him and started
to run.

"He's going to the station," said
Max. "Quick! Let's follow him and
get the egg back." They slipped and
scrambled down the steep path.

At last, they reached the station.
Wilma ran up to the man.

"We saw you take an egg from the
eagle's nest," she said.

The man was angry. "I didn't take
an egg," he said, and he opened his
bag. There was no egg inside.

Suddenly, there was a shout.

"One of the climbers has fallen!" said Max. "We must call the Mountain Rescue Team."

Wilma ran to blow the horn, but
the man tried to stop her.

"Give me that horn!" he shouted,
but Wilma pulled it away from him.

Wilma looked in the horn. "He's
hidden the egg in here!" she said.

The man started to run but Biff
tripped him up . . . CRASH!

Max took the egg and wrapped it
in his jacket to keep it warm.

Then Wilma blew the horn.

BOOM! . . . BOOM! . . . BOOM!

The Mountain Rescue helicopter
flew into the sky. Everyone cheered
as the climber was lifted to safety.

The helicopter landed and Max
showed Uncle Hans the eagle's egg.
"We must put the egg back before
it gets cold," said Uncle Hans.

Uncle Hans climbed up to the nest
and put the egg back. The eagle saw
the egg and flew back to her nest.

Three big feathers floated gently
down to the children.

"The eagle is saying thank you,"
said Biff, as the magic key glowed.

"Look! There's a wooden horn
on your music box now," said
Wilma. "How did it get there?"

"It must be magic," smiled Biff.

Talk about the story

What was
the big wooden horn
used for?

How do you
think the children
felt when the man
showed them his
empty bag?

Why did Max
wrap the egg in
his jacket?

How would you
feel if you saw someone
steal something?

A maze

Help Uncle Hans put the egg back.

Read with Biff, Chip and Kipper
The UK's best-selling home reading series

Phonics   First Stories

	Phonics				First Stories			
Level 1 Getting ready to read	Kipper's Alphabet I Spy	Chip's Letter Sounds	Biff's Wonder Words	Floppy's Fun Phonics	Get On	Floppy Did This!	Up You Go	Six in a Bed
Level 2 Starting to read	I am Kipper	Cat in a Bag	The Red Hen	The Fizz-Buzz	Funny Fish	Silly Races!	The Snowman	Dad's Birthday
Level 3 Becoming a reader	Such a Fuss	Shops	The Sing Song	The Backpack	Poor Old Rabbit	I Can Trick a Tiger	Super Dad	Floppy and the Bone
Level 4 Developing as a reader	Wet Feet	The Moon Jet	The Red Coat	Quick! Quick!	Missing!	The Raft Race	Dragon Danger	The Spaceship
Level 5 Building confidence in reading	Egg Fried Rice	Craig Saves the Day	Seasick	Dolphin Rescue	Hungry Floppy	Husky Adventure	Trapped!	Looking after Gran
Level 6 Reading with confidence	Gran's New Blue Shoes	Ice City	Save Pudding Wood	Uncle Max	Hairy-Scary Monster	Mountain Rescue	The Lost Voice	Secret of the Sands

Phonics stories help children practise their sounds and letters, as they learn to do in school.

First Stories have been specially written to provide practice in reading everyday language.

Read with Biff, Chip and Kipper Collections:

2 Phonics and 2 First Stories in every collection

 Up You Go and Other Stories

 Six in a Bed and Other Stories

 Funny Fish and Other Stories

 The Fizz-Buzz and Other Stories

 Floppy and the Bone and Other Stories

I Can Trick a Tiger and Other Stories

 The Moon Jet and Other Stories

 Dragon Danger and Other Stories

 Husky Adventure and Other Stories

 Looking After Gran and Other Stories

 Hairy-Scary Monster and Other Stories

 Secret of the Sands and Other Stories

Phonics support

Flashcards are a really fun way to practise phonics and build reading skills. Age 3+

My Phonics Kit is designed to support you and your child as you practise phonics together at home. It includes stickers, workbooks, interactive eBooks, support for parents and more! Age 5+

Read Write Inc. Phonics: A range of fun rhyming stories to support decoding skills. Age 4+

Songbirds Phonics: Lively and engaging phonics stories from Children's Laureate, Julia Donaldson. Age 4+

Help your child's reading with essential tips, advice on phonics and free eBooks
www.oxfordowl.co.uk